Safari
Dot-to-Dot
Adventure

Published by Top That! Publishing plc
Tide Mill Way, Woodbridge, Suffolk, IP12 IAP, UK
Copyright © 2011 Top That! Publishing plc
All rights reserved.
2 4 6 8 9 7 5 3 1
Printed and bound in China

Max and Molly are going on an African safari for their summer holiday this year.

When they arrive in Africa, Max and Molly are welcomed by a man called Jack. He will be their holiday guide.

How did Max and Molly travel to Africa?
Join the dots to find out!

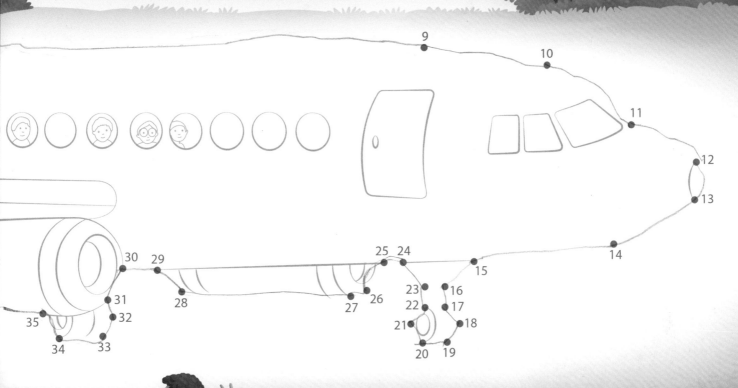

After a long and dusty drive in Jack's jeep, Max and Molly stop and set up camp for the night.

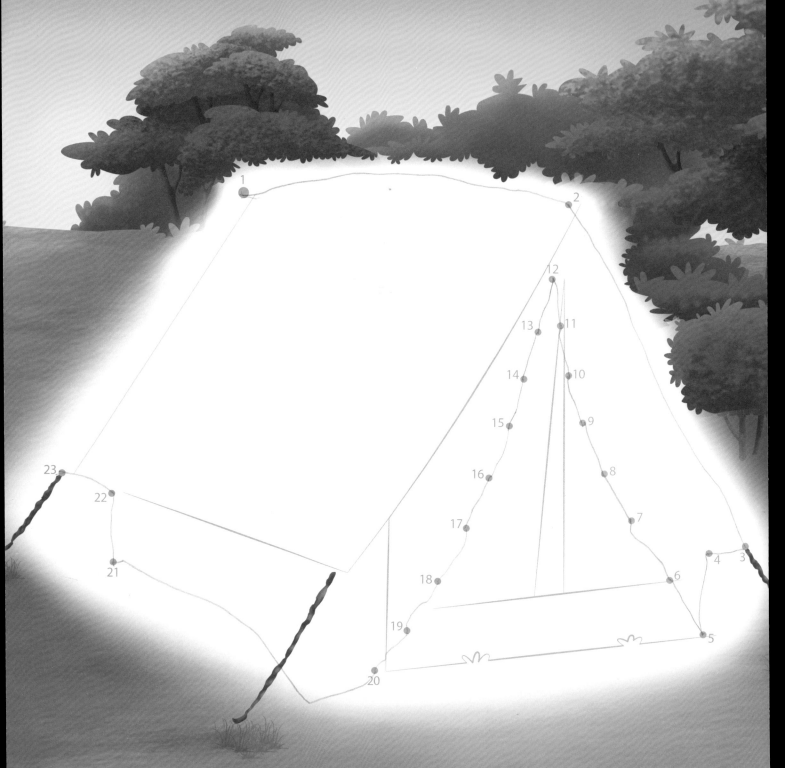

Can you help them?
Join the dots to complete the tent.

It is getting dark, so Max and Molly gather
firewood for Jack, who is making a
campfire to cook sausages
for dinner.

Who else is helping them with the dinner?
Join the dots to find out!

Early the next morning, Max and Molly visit a watering hole. Jack says that this is a really good place to spot animals who gather for a drink.

Jack is right! Who can you spot drinking at the watering hole and what animal is lurking in the water? Join the dots to find out!

Close to the watering hole, Max and Molly come across a group of acacia trees. Jack explains that the trees are covered with prickly thorns.

One animal is able to feed on the prickly, green trees, as it has a special, rough tongue and a very long neck to reach up into the high branches.

Can you guess what the animal is?
Join the dots to find out!

That afternoon Max spots some animals relaxing in the shade. Molly watches some young cubs playing rough-and-tumble games!

What family of animals have gathered here? Join the dots to find out!

Soon, it's time to return to camp for the night. Max and Molly talk non-stop about the animals they have seen already. They can't wait to continue their adventure tomorrow!

The next day, Max and Molly discover a pair of animals grunting and squealing as they bathe in the sticky mud. Jack tells the children that the mud helps to keep them cool and protects their skin from the hot sun.

All of the commotion has alerted another group of animals. They emerge from their den and stand up tall, on their hind legs, to look out for danger.

What animals are covered in sticky mud, and who are looking out for danger?
Join the dots to find out!

Next, Jack drives Max and Molly down to a river.
Molly sees some beautiful pink birds standing in the
shallows. Some are standing on one leg.

What birds are enjoying
the cool river water?
Join the dots to find out!

Then, Max spots some animals in the deeper water. These animals are big, but only their heads are visible above the water!

What large animals like to keep cool by submerging themselves in water? Join the dots to find out!

Later, Jack points out an animal on a branch of a nearby tree. It is almost completely camouflaged in the dappled sunlight.

What animal is hidden in the tree? Join the dots to find out!

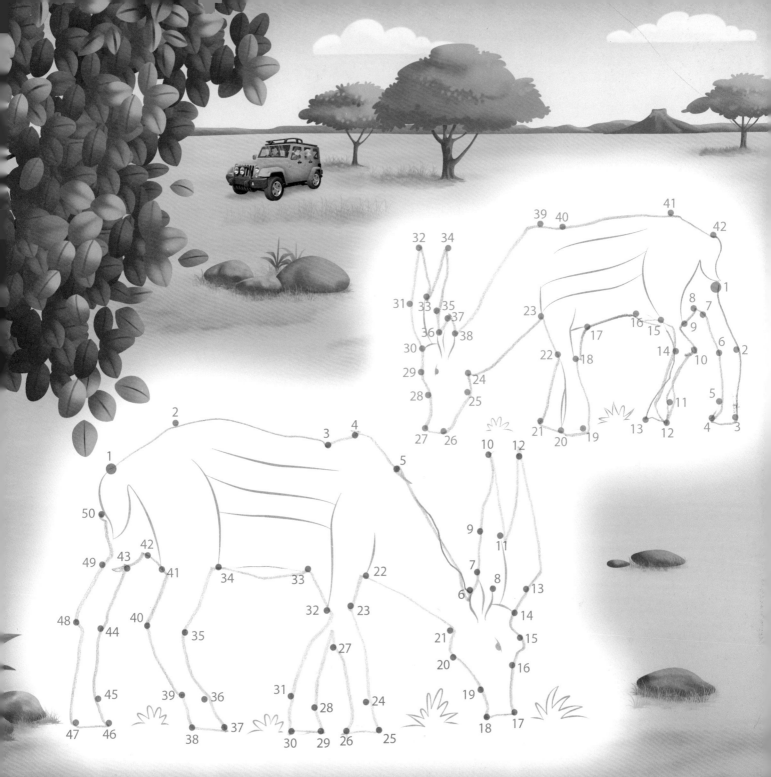

Nearby, a herd of animals are grazing on the grassy plains. Jack tells Max and Molly that these animals can run very fast.

What agile animals are grazing on grass?
Join the dots to find out!

High in the sky above them, large birds are circling around and around. Jack explains that these birds are scavengers looking for food.

Who are these scavengers of the sky?
Join the dots to find out!

It is the end of another exciting day and Max and Molly head back to camp for the night. They are both very tired, and soon fall fast asleep.

On Max and Molly's last day, they come across huge, grey animals, with big ears and long noses. Jack says that these animals use their noses to suck up water.

What animals use their noses to drink? Join the dots to find out!

Suddenly, something bumps the back of the jeep and Max and Molly turn around quickly and look out of the window. It is another large, strong animal with two horns on top of its nose!

What could this angry animal be? Join the dots to find out!

Max and Molly decide to end their holiday with a hot air balloon ride. From the balloon's basket, they gaze down at all of the animals on Africa's plains.

Can you complete the balloon by joining the dots?

As the sun sets over the savannah, the balloon drifts slowly over a rainforest and Max and Molly spot some brightly coloured exotic birds. They listen to the birds calling to each other from the high treetops.

What squawking birds did they see?
Join the dots to find out!

Back at home, Max and Molly look at their holiday photos and talk about the animals that they have seen. Did you identify all of the animals Max and Molly saw on their adventure?

Monkey

Wildebeest

Crocodile

Giraffe

Warthog

Lion

Meerkat

Flamingo

Leopard

Hippopotamus

Vulture

Gazelle

Elephant

Rhinoceros

Toucan

Macaw